C000152268

MAKING THE GRADE · G

EASY POPULAR PIECES FOR YOUNG CLARINETTISTS SELECTED AND ARRANGED BY JERRY LANNIN

CLARINET PART

Exclusive Distributors:
Music Sales Limited
Newmarket Road, Bury St. Edmunds, Suffolk IP33 3YB.
This book © copyright 1992 Chester Music.
ISBN 0-7119-2944-0
Order No. CH60072
Cover designed by Pemberton and Whitefoord
Typeset by Pemberton and Whitefoord
Printed in the United Kingdom by
Caligraving Limited, Thetford, Norfolk.

WARNING: the photocopying of any pages of this publication is illegal.
If copies are made in breach of copyright, the Publisher will,
where possible, sue for damages.

Chester Music
(A division of Music Sales Limited)
8/9 Frith Street, London W1V 5TZ.

THE INCREDIBLE HULK (THEME FROM)

Composed by Joe Harnell.

This theme from the TV series is a wistful and attractive melody, which reflects the gentle side of the Hulk's nature.
Try not to cut any phrases short before you breathe.

© Copyright 1977 MCA Music (a division of MCA Incorporated).
MCA Music Limited, 77 Fulham Palace Road, London W6 for the world excluding North, South and Central America, Japan, Australasia and the Philippines.
All Rights Reserved. International Copyright Secured.

YESTERDAY

Words & Music by John Lennon & Paul McCartney.

Most peoples' favourite Beatles song. Notice the C sharp and D sharp in the ascending
scale of E melodic minor (bar 4), followed by the C and D naturals in the descending scale.

© Copyright 1965 Northern Songs, under Licence to
MCA Music Limited, 77 Fulham Palace Road, London W6.
All Rights Reserved. International Copyright Secured.

EL CONDOR PASA (IF I COULD)

Musical Arrangement by J. Milchberg & D. Robles. English Lyric by Paul Simon.

This is a traditional melody from South America, made popular by Simon and Garfunkel.
Keep a very steady tempo.

© Copyright 1933, 1963, 1970 Edward B. Marks Music Corporation and Jorge Milchberg.
English Lyric Copyright 1970 Charing Cross Music Incorporated.
All Rights Reserved. International Copyright Secured.

SUMMERTIME

Music by George Gershwin.

'Summertime' is probably Gershwin's most famous tune. The notes aren't difficult,
but be careful that you play the correct rhythm in bars 11 and 12. Don't let the final D go flat.

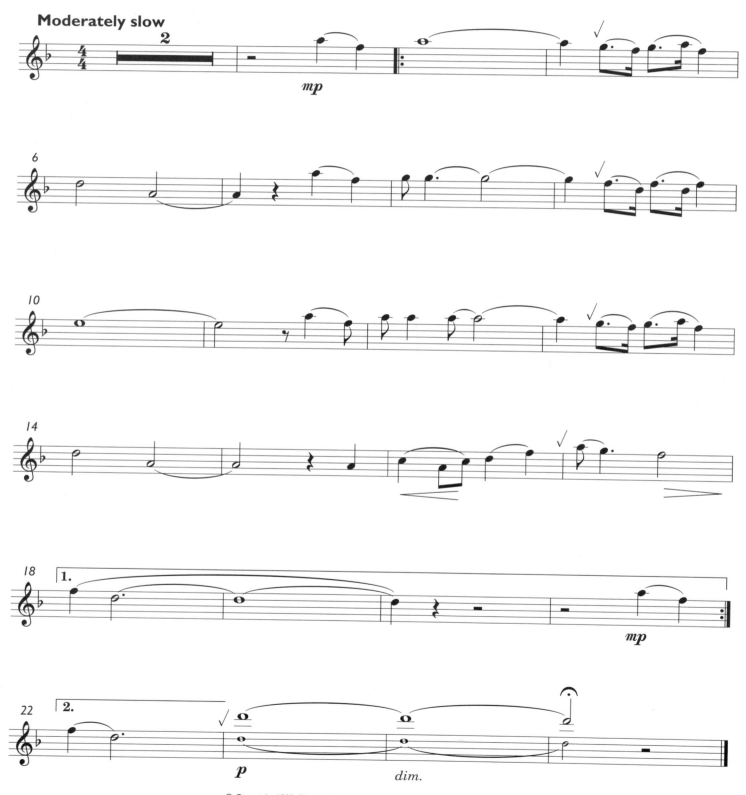

© Copyright 1992 Chester Music Limited, 8/9 Frith Street, London W1.
All Rights Reserved. International Copyright Secured.

ITSY BITSY, TEENIE WEENIE, YELLOW POLKADOT BIKINI

Words & Music by Lee Pockriss & Paul J. Vance.

If you want to leave out the spoken sections, you can cut from the first beat of bar 10 to the second beat of bar 12, and cut bar 22 completely. Watch out for the $\frac{2}{4}$ bar.

© Copyright 1960 Paul J. Vance Publishing Corporation &
Emily Music Corporation, USA. Campbell Connelly & Company Limited, 8/9 Frith Street, London W1.
All Rights Reserved. International Copyright Secured.

BRIDGE OVER TROUBLED WATER

Words & Music by Paul Simon.

Here is Paul Simon's most enduring song.
Try for a full, rounded tone as the piece builds to a climax around bar 23.

© Copyright 1969 Paul Simon.
All Rights Reserved. International Copyright Secured.

I KNOW HIM SO WELL

Words & Music by Benny Andersson, Tim Rice & Bjorn Ulvaeus.

Many of the notes are slurred in pairs,

which should be practised carefully to ensure that the second note of each pair 'speaks' clearly.

© Copyright 1984 3 Knights Limited. Copyright administered for the world by Union Songs AB, Stockholm, Sweden.
Bocu Music Limited, I Wyndham Yard, Wyndham Place, London WI for the UK and Eire.
All Rights Reserved. International Copyright Secured.

BIRDIE SONG/BIRDIE DANCE

Words & Music by Werner Thomas & Terry Rendall.

Articulate the quavers in the first section clearly, almost *staccato*,
to contrast with the smoothly phrased second part.

© Copyright 1973 Intervox Music, Pierstraat 322 2550 Kontich, Belgium.
All rights for the British Isles Colonies and Republic of Ireland controlled by The Valentine Music Group, 7 Garrick Street, London WC2.
All Rights Reserved. International Copyright Secured.

JEANIE WITH THE LIGHT BROWN HAIR

Words & Music by Stephen Foster.

This song needs really expressive playing.
Be particularly careful of the slurred ninth (F to G) in bar 14. The G should be really soft.

© Copyright 1992 Chester Music Limited, 8/9 Frith Street, London W1.
All Rights Reserved. International Copyright Secured.

HE AIN'T HEAVY HE'S MY BROTHER

Words by Bob Russell. Music by Bobby Scott.

Some of the rhythms are a bit tricky in this piece. If you have some trouble with them,
practise each phrase slightly slower, counting in quavers. Be careful to count the rests in bar 21.

© Copyright 1969 by Harrison Music Corporation, USA & Jenny Music.
Chelsea Music Publishing Company Limited, 70 Gloucester Place, London W1H 4AJ/Jenny Music.
All Rights Reserved. International Copyright Secured.

AMERICA

Music by Leonard Bernstein. Lyrics by Stephen Sondheim.

In this lively number from 'West Side Story' the time signature alternates between $\frac{6}{8}$ and $\frac{3}{4}$;
you will need to keep this clearly in mind in bars 17 to 25.

© Copyright 1957 (Renewed) by Leonard Bernstein & Stephen Sondheim. Jalni Publications Incorporated/Boosey & Hawkes Incorporated, USA & Canadian publisher.
G. Schirmer Incorporated, worldwide print rights & publisher for rest of the World. G. Schirmer Limited/Campbell Connelly & Company Limited, 8/9 Frith Street, London W1V 5TZ.
All Rights Reserved. International Copyright Secured.

BERGERAC

Composed by George Fenton.

Another TV theme, which here makes a substantial concert piece. The main theme is repeated an octave higher. Remember that D. 𝄋 al ⊕ Coda means 'Go back to the sign, then take the coda'.

© Copyright 1981 Shogun Music/Eaton Music Limited, 8 West Eaton Place, London SW1.
All Rights Reserved. International Copyright Secured.

THE ENTERTAINER

.By Scott Joplin.

This piano rag featured in the film 'The Sting'. Make sure you keep a very steady tempo.
You will find that the piece is quite a test of stamina.

© Copyright 1992 Chester Music Limited, 8/9 Frith Street, London W1.
All Rights Reserved. International Copyright Secured.

2/95 (19663)

MAKING THE GRADE · GRADE 3

EASY POPULAR PIECES FOR YOUNG CLARINETTISTS SELECTED AND ARRANGED BY JERRY LANNING EDITED. BY MARTIN FRITH

Exclusive Distributors:
Music Sales Limited
Newmarket Road, Bury St. Edmunds, Suffolk IP33 3YB.
This book © copyright 1992 Chester Music.
ISBN 0-7119-2944-0
Order No. CH60072
Cover designed by Pemberton and Whitefoord
Typeset by Pemberton and Whitefoord
Printed in the United Kingdom by
Caligraving Limited, Thetford, Norfolk.

WARNING: the photocopying of any pages of this publication is illegal.
If copies are made in breach of copyright, the Publisher will,
where possible, sue for damages.

Chester Music

(A division of Music Sales Limited)
8/9 Frith Street, London W1V 5TZ.

INTRODUCTION

This collection of 13 popular tunes has been carefully arranged and graded to provide attractive teaching repertoire for young clarinettists. The familiarity of the material will stimulate pupils' enthusiasm and encourage their practice.

The technical demands of the solo part increase progressively up to the standard of Associated Board Grade 3. The piano accompaniments are simple yet effective and should be within the range of most pianists.

Breath marks are given throughout, showing the most musically desirable places to take a breath. Students may also need to take additional breaths when learning a piece or practising at a slower tempo, and suitable opportunities are indicated by breath marks in brackets.

THE INCREDIBLE HULK (THEME FROM)

Composed by Joe Harnell.

This theme from the TV series is a wistful and attractive melody, which reflects the gentle side of the Hulk's nature.
Try not to cut any phrases short before you breathe.

© Copyright 1977 MCA Music (a division of MCA Incorporated).
MCA Music Limited, 77 Fulham Palace Road, London W6 for the world excluding North, South and Central America, Japan, Australasia and the Philippines.
All Rights Reserved. International Copyright Secured.

YESTERDAY

Words & Music by John Lennon & Paul McCartney.

Most peoples' favourite Beatles song. Notice the C sharp and D sharp in the ascending
scale of E melodic minor (bar 4), followed by the C and D naturals in the descending scale.

© Copyright 1965 Northern Songs, under Licence to
MCA Music Limited, 77 Fulham Palace Road, London W6.
All Rights Reserved. International Copyright Secured.

7

EL CONDOR PASA (IF I COULD)

Musical Arrangement by J. Milchberg & D. Robles. English Lyric by Paul Simon.

This is a traditional melody from South America, made popular by Simon and Garfunkel.

Keep a very steady tempo.

© Copyright 1933, 1963, 1970 Edward B. Marks Music Corporation and Jorge Milchberg.
English Lyric Copyright 1970 Charing Cross Music Incorporated.
All Rights Reserved. International Copyright Secured.

SUMMERTIME

Music by George Gershwin.

'Summertime' is probably Gershwin's most famous tune. The notes aren't difficult,
but be careful that you play the correct rhythm in bars 11 and 12. Don't let the final D go flat.

Moderately slow

© Copyright 1992 Chester Music Limited, 8/9 Frith Street, London W1.
All Rights Reserved. International Copyright Secured.

ITSY BITSY, TEENIE WEENIE, YELLOW POLKADOT BIKINI

Words & Music by Lee Pockriss & Paul J. Vance.

If you want to leave out the spoken sections, you can cut from the first beat of bar 10 to the second beat of bar 12, and cut bar 22 completely. Watch out for the $\frac{2}{4}$ bar.

© Copyright 1960 Paul J. Vance Publishing Corporation & Emily Music Corporation, USA. Campbell Connelly & Company Limited, 8/9 Frith Street, London W1. All Rights Reserved. International Copyright Secured.

Two, three, four,

Stick a - round we'll tell you more.

BRIDGE OVER TROUBLED WATER

Words & Music by Paul Simon.

Here is Paul Simon's most enduring song.
Try for a full, rounded tone as the piece builds to a climax around bar 23.

Not too fast

© Copyright 1969 Paul Simon.
All Rights Reserved. International Copyright Secured.

I KNOW HIM SO WELL

Words & Music by Benny Andersson, Tim Rice & Bjorn Ulvaeus.

Many of the notes are slurred in pairs,
which should be practised carefully to ensure that the second note of each pair 'speaks' clearly.

© Copyright 1984 3 Knights Limited. Copyright administered for the world by Union Songs AB, Stockholm, Sweden.
Bocu Music Limited, 1 Wyndham Yard, Wyndham Place, London W1 for the UK and Eire.
All Rights Reserved. International Copyright Secured.

BIRDIE SONG/BIRDIE DANCE

Words & Music by Werner Thomas & Terry Rendall.

Articulate the quavers in the first section clearly, almost *staccato*,
to contrast with the smoothly phrased second part.

© Copyright 1973 Intervox Music, Pierstraat 322 2550 Kontich, Belgium.
All rights for the British Isles Colonies and Republic of Ireland controlled by The Valentine Music Group, 7 Garrick Street, London WC2.
All Rights Reserved. International Copyright Secured.

19

JEANIE WITH THE LIGHT BROWN HAIR

Words & Music by Stephen Foster.

This song needs really expressive playing.

Be particularly careful of the slurred ninth (F to G) in bar 14. The G should be really soft.

© Copyright 1992 Chester Music Limited, 8/9 Frith Street, London W1.
All Rights Reserved. International Copyright Secured.

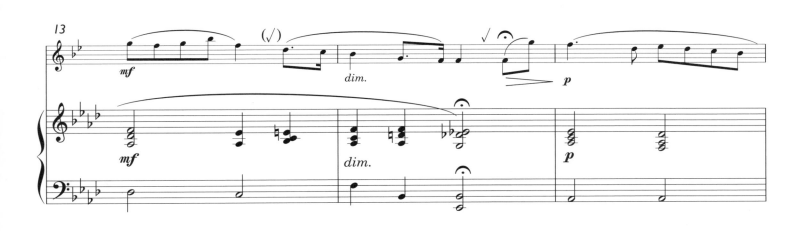

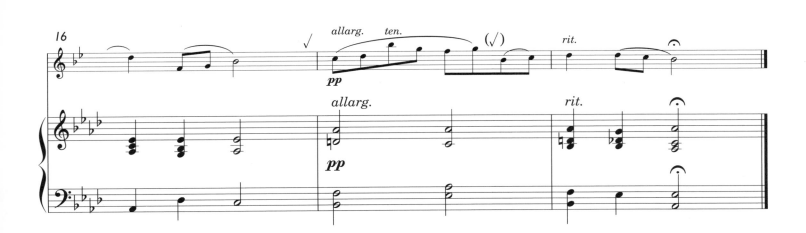

HE AIN'T HEAVY HE'S MY BROTHER

Words by Bob Russell. Music by Bobby Scott.

Some of the rhythms are a bit tricky in this piece. If you have some trouble with them,
practise each phrase slightly slower, counting in quavers. Be careful to count the rests in bar 21.

© Copyright 1969 by Harrison Music Corporation, USA & Jenny Music.
Chelsea Music Publishing Company Limited, 70 Gloucester Place, London W1H 4AJ/Jenny Music.
All Rights Reserved. International Copyright Secured.

AMERICA

Music by Leonard Bernstein. Lyrics by Stephen Sondheim

In this lively number from 'West Side Story' the time signature alternates between $\frac{6}{8}$ and $\frac{3}{4}$;
you will need to keep this clearly in mind in bars 17 to 25.

© Copyright 1957 (Renewed) by Leonard Bernstein & Stephen Sondheim. Jalni Publications Incorporated/Boosey & Hawkes Incorporated, USA & Canadian publisher.
G. Schirmer Incorporated, worldwide print rights & publisher for rest of the World. G. Schirmer Limited/Campbell Connelly & Company Limited, 8/9 Frith Street, London W1V 5TZ.
All Rights Reserved. International Copyright Secured.

BERGERAC

Composed by George Fenton.

Another TV theme, which here makes a substantial concert piece. The main theme is repeated an octave higher. Remember that D. ℅ al ⊕ Coda means 'Go back to the sign, then take the coda'.

Moderately bright

© Copyright 1981 Shogun Music/Eaton Music Limited, 8 West Eaton Place, London SW1.
All Rights Reserved. International Copyright Secured.

THE ENTERTAINER

By Scott Joplin.

This piano rag featured in the film 'The Sting'. Make sure you keep a very steady tempo.
You will find that the piece is quite a test of stamina.

© Copyright 1992 Chester Music Limited, 8/9 Frith Street, London W1.
All Rights Reserved. International Copyright Secured.

2/95 (19663)